The Queen Machine

Because everything you need was, is, and will always be within you.

Dedication

To my mom - for crying when I said yes to pageantry and
no to med school but for supporting me unequivocally
anyway. I love you.

And to every kid out there (kids at heart included) - who
wish they had something different, were someone different,
or had different circumstances...

To those kids who are told to change who they are but
change the world instead...

way to persist, I'm proud of you.

Can you find the hidden crown on every page?

Our teacher, Mrs. Trimbo, is the nicest and quirkiest teacher in our school.

She has bright blue hair, cowboy boots, and sings the morning announcements.

When Mrs. Trimbo introduced the Queen Machine to our 3rd grade class, Michaela, Brooke, and I all gasped out loud at the same time.

It was big, beautiful, and unlike anything I had ever seen!

This classroom honors the Cheyenne native lands we learn on.

What is that?

She said,

I'm so glad you asked, Amrita. This is the Queen Machine. Everyone in this room has the potential to be a beautiful queen. This machine will let you know when you have earned that title!

Ever since we were little, we had dreamt of being queens, and now we had our chance in real life. Queens are just so...

POWERFUL!

Mrs. Trimbo smiled and said,

Okay everyone, you don't have to get in, but when you're ready, it will be here for you.

Everybody in class was nervous to try it. What if we weren't good enough? What if the machine told us we couldn't be queens after all? We would be so sad.

Mrs.Trimbo, I think I'm ready.

Finally, when no one else came forward, I raised my hand and said...

Count me in, Mrs. Trimbo!

Me too, Mrs. Trimbo!

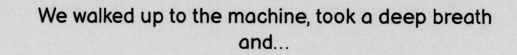

We walked up to the machine, took a deep breath
and...

...then we heard Bobby, the
meanest boy in our class, laugh and say,

Amrita, you can't be a
queen! You are short, have
pimples, and the food you
bring for lunch smells
terrible!

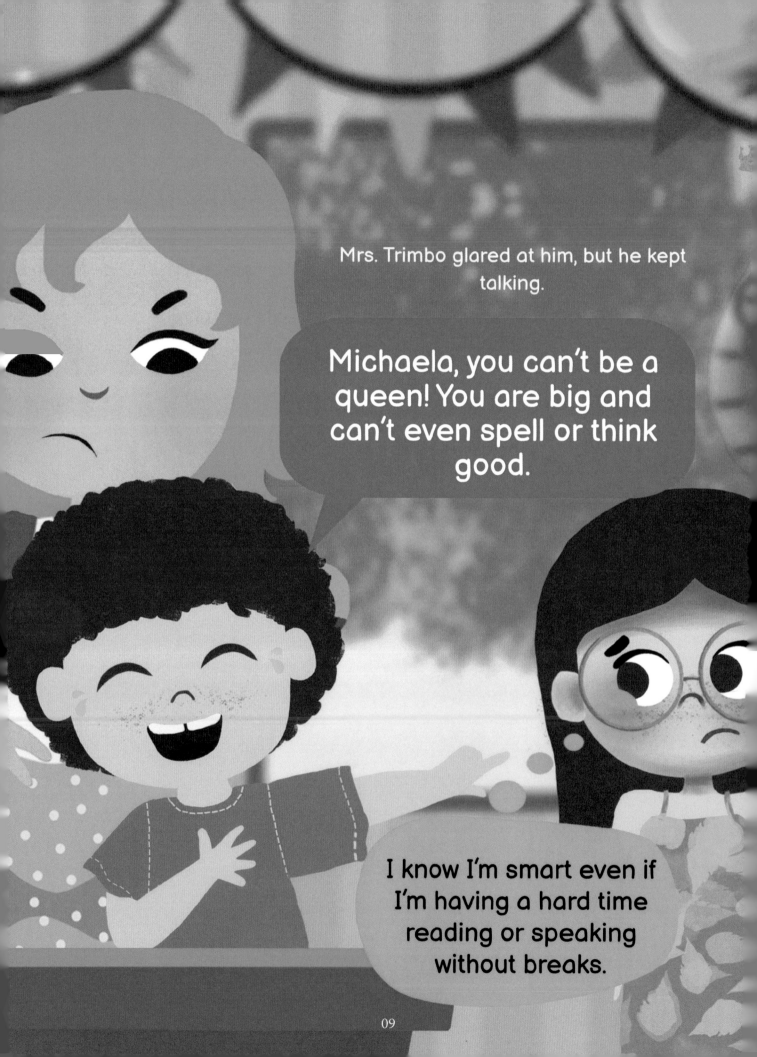

Mrs. Trimbo glared at him, but he kept talking.

Michaela, you can't be a queen! You are big and can't even spell or think good.

I know I'm smart even if I'm having a hard time reading or speaking without breaks.

As Mrs. Trimbo walked over to Bobby,
he shouted out,

Brooke you can't be a
queen! Your hair is all frizzy,
your skin is super dark, and
you talk funny!

Mrs. Trimbo sent him
to the principal for
being mean to us.

10

Brooke, Michaela, and I were embarrassed and stepped away from the Queen Machine.

Could that boy be right? Were we not meant to be queens?

All that week, we tried to change ourselves in hopes that we could try the Queen Machine.

Brooke straightened her hair and tried to stay out of the sunlight to make her skin lighter.

I didn't tell her, but I really liked her curls and the color of her skin.

Michaela wore very different clothes and stopped talking in class so that no one would notice her.

This was too bad because I always liked it when she read out loud and I loved her sense of style.

She always made me smile.

MY ALPHABETS

And I made myself much taller, covered up all of my pimples, straightened my hair, and even started eating the school lunches.

MY LUNCH NOW

Fries

Ranch Dip

Apple Juice

Apple

PB and J sandwich

Me no

Michaela and Brooke said they were sad because they liked when I shared food with them.

Now, we were ready.

The next morning, we all RUSHED to go inside the machine, hoping to come out with a crown.

Mrs. Trimbo, Mrs. Trimbo! Watch me! Here I go into the machine!

SWOOOOOSH

BANG!

QUEEN
MACHINE

GO

STOP

I heard a SWOOSH and a BANG.

Then the machine paused and ZOOOOOMP.

Out came.....

NOTHING?

16

I checked all around the machine...
I looked underneath it.

QUEEN
MACHINE

Where is my crown?

Brooke and Michaela went through the machine. Each time....

We got NOTHING.

Maybe the machine was broken. Or, maybe none of us were meant to be queens.

Every day, we stared at the Queen Machine, but we were too scared to try it again.

One day as we were walking through the hallway, we saw a beautiful girl in a grade above us. She was rolling down the hallway and had a crown on.

"Is that a Queen's crown?" we asked her.

"Si," she said. I spoke a little Spanish so I knew that meant yes.

"What did you change about yourself to get it?" we asked.

"Nada," she replied, smiling, and rolled away to class.

Wait a second... "nada" means "nothing?"

We were confused, so we went to Mrs.Trimbo's class.
She was not there, but she left something on her desk for us.
It read:

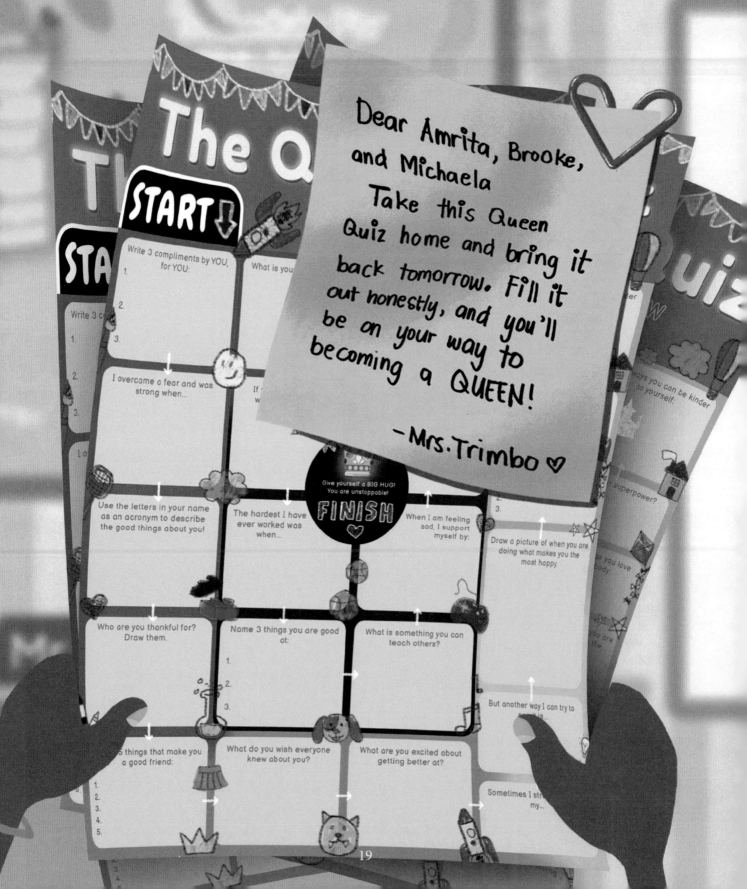

Dear Amrita, Brooke, and Michaela
Take this Queen Quiz home and bring it back tomorrow. Fill it out honestly, and you'll be on your way to becoming a QUEEN!

— Mrs.Trimbo ♡

That night I took the Queen Quiz. It was very hard to answer all the questions.

I sat upside down with it.

I fell asleep on it.

I accidentally spilled my lemonade on it.

I even took it in the bathroom with me.

The questions on it were not like any quiz I had ever taken.

They were all about things I liked about myself.

The more I thought about it, the more I realized everything about myself was special, and I never have to change anything.

After I filled it out, I finally understood...

A crown might show OTHERS I'm a queen but the only thing that can ACTUALLY make me a queen is truly and fully LOVING everything (even the funny things!) that make me...ME!

The next day I went back to Mrs.Trimbo and handed her my quiz. She looked at me, smiled, and said,

Amrita, I think you're finally ready.

When I stepped into the Queen Machine, I felt confident, I felt happy with myself.This time holding my Queen Quiz, I knew that no matter what happened, I was special.

I heard a SWOOSH and a BOOM and a big PUFF!

I didn't feel any different, but suddenly, on my head was a...

I jumped the highest I had ever jumped.

I felt the best I have ever felt! And when I walked out of the machine, Brooke and Michaela were right there to hug me!

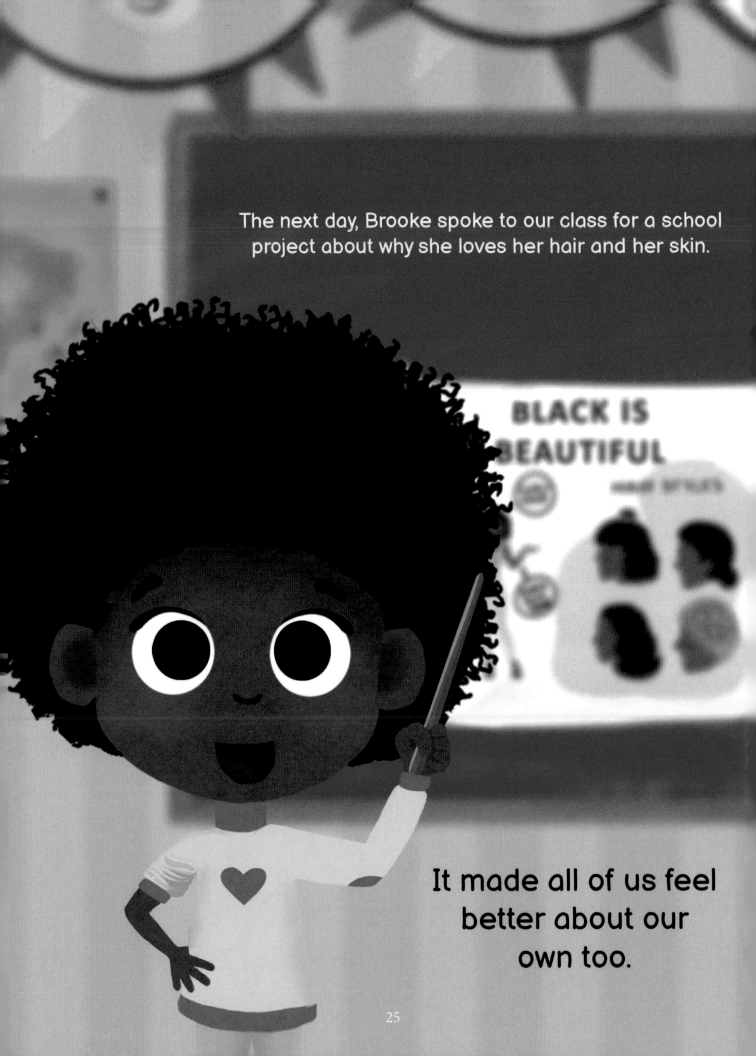

The next day, Brooke spoke to our class for a school project about why she loves her hair and her skin.

BLACK IS
BEAUTIFUL

It made all of us feel better about our own too.

I saw Brooke walk into the machine with her Queen Quiz filled out.
I suddenly heard a big PUFF. Brooke came out with a crown!

A few days after, Michaela painted "I love myself because I_____" stickers for everyone in the school. She wore them too!

People had to fill then in with their favorite trait about themselves!

I even saw Mrs. Trimbo wearing one!

I saw Michaela go into the machine that day. I saw her come out with the biggest smile... this time, with a Queen Quiz in her hands and a crown on her head.

We went back to Mrs. Trimbo to show her what we learned through our new crowns.

We all did it.

We were all queens the entire time!

We just have to look inside ourselves to find it and celebrate it... and THAT is what takes time.

Mrs. Trimbo laughed and said,

See? You all were queens the entire time, and all you had to do was to believe it yourself!

Then, Mrs. Trimbo pulled out her crown from under her desk. She was a queen all along too!

After that, Michaela, Brooke, and I passed out queen quizzes to every kid we met, hoping that they would take it and knowing that they were ready to become whoever they dreamed of becoming.

SPEAKING UP
FOR YOURSELF
with Michaela

Be Better

And from that day
on, if anyone said
something mean
to us, we knew it
couldn't hurt us.

We were real queens,
and we were happy
with ourselves, just the
way we were.

We wanted to give YOU all the secrets we learned, including the Queen Quiz!

You're ready to be a queen too.

Trust me, the Queen Machine is waiting for you to realize your worth, just like it did with me and my friends!

The Queen Quiz

START ⬇

Follow the RAINBOW
to finish the quiz!

Write 3 compliments by YOU, for YOU:

1.

2.

3.

What is your BIGGEST goal?

What could others learn from you to make the world a better place?

List 4 ways you can be kinder to yourself:

1.

2.

3.

4.

I overcame a fear and was strong when...

If you weren't afraid, what would you do?

"I'm a QUEEN because..."

What is your superpower?

What are 3 things you love about your body:

1.

2.

3.

Give yourself a BIG HUG!
You are unstoppable!

FINISH
♥

Use the letters in your name as an acronym to describe the good things about you!

The hardest I have ever worked was when...

When I am feeling sad, I support myself by:

Draw a picture of when you are doing what makes you the most happy.

Who are you thankful for? Draw them.

Name 3 things you are good at:

1.

2.

3.

What is something you can teach others?

But another way I can try to see it is...

Name 5 things that make you a good friend:

1.

2.

3.

4.

5.

What do you wish everyone knew about you?

What are you excited about getting better at?

Sometimes I struggle loving my...

RESOURCE PAGE

The Statistics:

- More than 90% of kids wish they could change something about their appearance. *(Source: Psychology Today)*
- 80% of people claim poor body image issues are linked back to negative statements by family members *(Source: Harley Therapy)*
- You are your child's first teacher. Children who feel their parents are dissatisfied with them in any way are more likely to feel the same way about themselves as a result. *(Source: Common Sense)*

Children with LOW self-esteem may...	Children with HIGH self-esteem may...
Find it difficult to form and grow relationships; feel unlikeable or isolated	Are comfortable and secure in developing relationships
Have a hard time dealing with failure; they may verbally show this by saying negative statements (i.e. "I'm dumb" or "I can't do anything right," etc.)	Act independently and are able to disassociate mistakes from their view of themselves
Are more likely to be targets of bullying or be bullies themselves; often seek the approval of others	Have courage to make good choices, even in the face of peer pressure
Quit on goals or struggle developing them at all	Persist until they reach their goals
Avoid changes or trying new things.	Are excited to take risks and experience changes

Source: Understood For All Inc.

Effects of low self-esteem in

- **Imposter Syndrome**
  - Children, especially girls, are more vulnerable to "impostor feelings," feeling unworthy of goals or incapable of reaching their dreams.

  - Therefore, helping kids find role models and mentors that look like theirs or have experiences like them allows children to reframe any psychological belief they may have that screams "no, not me."

- **Self-Dissatisfaction**
  - Kids who struggle with low self-esteem are at risk for depression, anxiety, eating disorders, and self-harm.

  - Exposure to what is deemed "beautiful" or "handsome" has a profound effect on kids. The preservation of the internalization of these ideals needs must be stopped at homes. Psychologists recommend parents engage in regular discussions around body image, healthy friendships, as well as pressures children face outside of home.

- **Toxic Behaviors**
  - Some kids are also more likely to engage in isolation, self-blame, rumination, and crying, while others use aggression and violence when struggling with self-esteem.

  - Parents should set healthy and attainable expectations for their children, as well as implementing family activities to "embrace failures" and communicate openly about thoughts kids have before actions become habits.

The Strategy

DARE TO BE YOU - MATTHEW SYED
Teaches there is no such thing as "normal." Being "different" is both acceptable and needed.

MINDSET - CAROL DWECK
Teaches parents how to help children develop a "growth mentality" to keep them resilient and motivated in life.

THE BOOK YOU WISH YOUR PARENTS HAD READ - PHILIPPA PERRY
Addresses parental psychology, generational trauma, and exercises for growth to pass down to children.

ZOOTOPIA
The main character chases her dreams with a positive attitude despite everyone around her doubting her abilities.

INSIDE OUT
The self-esteem of children is often centered on their emotions. This movie helps kids learn to not dismiss or "handle" emotions, but work to understand and accept them.

DANCING IN THE LIGHT: THE JANET COLLINS STORY
The powerful story of the very first African American prima ballerina fighting her way to her biggest dreams without changing who she is.

PEACE OUT - CHANEL TSANG
A collection of short stories to help children develop tools to meditate and become more mindful.

GOODNIGHT STORIES FOR REBEL GIRLS - APPLE PODCAST
Highlighting powerful women throughout history who inspire us to "dream bigger, reach higher, and fight harder."

SELF ESTEEM - CHILDREN'S HOME SOCIETY OF CALIFORNIA
Developing the "nature" and "nurture" aspect of parenting to help children grow their confidence.

The Solution: Helpful Activities/Exercises to Help Build Children's Self-Esteem

- **The Being + Doing Ladder (Source: Center for Parenting Education)**
  - This ladder highlights the two parts of the equation that must be BALANCED to develop a child's confidence. "BEING" messages communicate unconditional positiveness and love.

  - For instance, "I love you," "You are so important to me," "I'm lucky for you." These can also be actionable like with hugs, gifts, and acts of service for kids (i.e. a nighttime story, etc.).

B	E	I	N	G
D	O	I	N	G

- "DOING" messages address competency and capabilities among children. These messages highlight potential and growth like "It was very thoughtful of you to do the dishes last night" or "I love how hard you worked on your project. Your persistence and eye for detail shine!"

- **Design Affirmations**
  - Create a list of positive "I AM" statements, or affirmations, with your child and attach it to a whiteboard or refrigerator door. Encourage repetition and regular returns to the affirmations to help children develop a healthy self-narrative.

- **Strength In Differences**
  - Work with your child on writing their "Superpowers," or "Strengths"

  - Make a list of all the ways they differ from their peers, family, classmates, people they know, as well as people they don't know. Next to that list, have them write down why each strength could be useful to them now or in the future

  - Draw a horizontal line underneath the list and ask your child to add other superpowers or strengths they can set goals of having.

Educator's Page

- Seven out of every ten girls believe they are "not good enough" or "do not measure up to others." This includes their physical appearance, personal traits, relationships, or academic performance. *(Source: Life Works)*
- One out of every five (20.2%) students report being bullied for their differences (National Center for Educational Statistics). Students who experience bullying are at increased risk for prolonged victimization, depression, anxiety, health issues including sleep difficulties, lower academic achievement, and dropping out of school. *(Source: Centers for Disease Control and Prevention)*

The Strategy

- **Self-Appreciation**

- Educators have a unique role in embracing the individuality of every student, providing accommodations where necessary, and ensuring each student feel respected. Communicating collectively to all students about "fairness" to ensure resentment does not foster and addressing issues as they arise helps create a healthy classroom.

    ✓ Student X is learning how to speak English and reads slower than her peers. The teacher communicates to the class how unique the gift of being bilingual is, and sets up peer partner reading groups to strengthen 1-1-connections as well as help build the confidence of each student.

- **Responsibility**

- Encouraging students to give to the community helps them develop a sense of pride and responsibility. Noticing unique strengths, passions, and ideas in students can help them transform those gifts into responsibilities they can appreciate and grow from.

    ✓ An animal-loving student who struggles with public speaking and social isolation is recruited by their teacher to manage the classroom fish. The student is tasked to mentor the class about taking care of the fish.

- **Self-Advocacy**

- Research shows students who are confident to speak in front of others develop greater self-confidence and problem solving skills in life. Helping facilitate activities that meet the needs of every student when it comes to self-advocacy will push students to learn healthy and helpful ways of communicating.

    ✓ A teacher works with Student A who struggles with blurting out answers to instead count to 10 before raising their hand. The teacher works with Student B who never raises their hand to prepare a short presentation on a topic of their choosing before a small group of their peers.

- **Coping with Mistakes/Failure**

    - Students rely on educators to develop relationships with failure. Remarks like, "How often do I have to repeat myself?" or "Were you listening carefully?" can be damaging to a student's self-esteem. Recognizing a student's perspective after a mistake is a helpful strategy: "I can see that those directions might have been too long and too confusing. Let's work on figuring it out together."

    ✓ A student doesn't get an answer right in class. Instead of moving on to another student immediately, the teacher says, "Let's review how to solve that problem" and uses the student's mistake as a teachable moment. On one hand, it highlights to students that mistakes are meant to be learned from and on the other, it helps clarify the solution to the problem for the class.

- **Providing Tools/Resources**

- A child can struggle at school with issues from life outside of school. Resources like access to counselors, presentations on abuse, sanitary products, and school nurses are critical. In order to destigmatize students asking for help, teachers should try to implement fun and/or secretive ways for students to get the help they need.

    A teacher sets aside 2-minute check-ins with students and listens to their week's struggles. Resources can be given immediately so the issues stay confidential, and the teacher is aware to follow-up on any concerns.

(Credits: The Inclusion Lab)

DO	DON'T
Learn how you can better support students with differemt backgrounds and implement ways guided by parents and students to ensure students feel respected and comfortable.	Don't ignore differences (race, religious, gender, ability, etc.) or expect every student to respond, act, or think similarly.
Work 1-on-1 with all students and identify ways to highlight their gifts and differences in positive ways and improve upon their weaknesses too.	Don't promote classroom competition for attention or praise. This includes allowing only certain students to gain experiences and have responsibilities.
Listen to bullied students, check-in afterwards to ensure the bullying stopped, provide school resources and give advice.	Don't ask bullied students to solve problems on their own, victim blame, wait to see if something changes organically, or accuse students of "tattling."

Source: David and Nixon (2010)

Congratulations! You found all the crowns!

Made in the USA
Middletown, DE
22 August 2021